BFE

BY JULIA CHO

DRAMATISTS
PLAY SERVICE
INC.

For Ed

BFE was commissioned and originally developed by New York Theatre Workshop. It subsequently received developmental workshops at Center Theatre Group/Mark Taper Forum's Asian Theater Workshop and New Works Festival; Seattle Rep/Hedgebrook Women Playwrights Festival, Seattle Repertory Theatre; The Goodman Theatre; Just Add Water/West, A Playwright's Festival, produced by Portland Center Stage; and the Cape Cod Theatre Project.

The world premiere of BFE was presented at the Long Wharf Theatre (Gordon Edelstein, Artistic Director; Michael Stotts, Managing Director) in New Haven, Connecticut, opening on April 20, 2005. The Long Wharf production subsequently premiered in New York City at Playwrights Horizons (Tim Sanford, Artistic Director; Leslie Marcus, Managing Director; William Russo, General Manager) in the Peter Jay Sharp Theater, opening on May 31, 2005. It was directed by Gordon Edelstein; the set design was by Takeshi Kata; the costume design was by Jayde Chabot; the lighting design was by Paul Whitaker; the sound design was by Andre J. Pluess and Ben Sussman; and the production stage manager was Linda Marvel. The cast was as follows:

PANNY .... Olivia Oguma
ISABEL .... Kate Rigg
LEFTY .... James Saito
NANCY .... Kel Martin
HUGO .... James McMenamin
EVVIE .... Karen Kandel
THE MAN .... Scott Hudson
JACK/THE GENERAL .... Jeremy Hollingworth
HAE-YOON .... Sue Jean Kim

CHARACTERS

PANNY: Fourteen. Asian-American.

ISABEL: Panny's mother, thirties. Asian-American.

LEFTY: Isabel's brother. A few years older than Isabel. Asian-American.

NANCY: Fifteen. Blonde.

HUGO: Twenty. White.

EVVIE: Short for Evelyn. Forty. African American.

THE MAN: A man of indeterminate age. Absolutely charming.

JACK/THE GENERAL: A young white male.

HAE-YOON: Fourteen. Asian.

PLACE

B.F.E.

TIME

Late nineties.

I'm the right size for love.

—*Stephen Dunn*

BFE

Scene 1

Lights up on Panny, a fourteen-year-old Asian-American girl.

PANNY. *(To us:)* Things happen all the time out here, things you can't explain. Like this girl I know, Sheila Lopez, said she was sitting in her backyard with her mom one night and she saw this burst of light in the sky. It was like a comet or something, this circle of light that started off small and then became huge before finally flattening out into a thin, white line that disappeared. And all this happened in like maybe the space of five seconds. Sheila swears it was a UFO but her mom, she was facing the other way, so she didn't see a thing.

Other stuff happens too. The older kids have keg parties, music playing off the back of someone's truck. Mr. Lindhart down the street goes walking early in the morning with a gun strapped to his belt because he says there are snakes out there and you never know. Sometimes he forgets he's wearing it and he'll go right off to the supermarket with it.

Every once in awhile, something bad will happen. A guy takes a girl out there and does bad things to her. And sometimes she walks out and sometimes she doesn't.

There are still rumors swirling around school about what happened to me. That I was taken by a Satanic cult. Or kidnapped by some kiddie porn ring. That I kicked out a window, or threw myself out of a moving car.

But none of those things are true. What is true, depends, like Sheila, her mom and the light in the sky, on which way you are facing. *(Lights shift.)*

It is exactly one month ago. Girls have been disappearing from my school. Today, we had a moment of silence in homeroom for Sherry Evans, who was the third most popular girl in school. I've just started my freshman year at Brimsdale High. It's a very dangerous time.

Scene 2

A drugstore magazine aisle. Panny sits on the floor reading a magazine. Nancy, fifteen, blonde and pretty is watching her as she stocks items on the shelf.

NANCY. Would you put that back?

PANNY. I'm reading.

NANCY. I'll get in trouble. My manager.

PANNY. Do you think I'd look good with this hair?

NANCY. Don't wrinkle it, you're wrinkling it.

PANNY. I'm not.

NANCY. You are. Shouldn't you be home?

PANNY. Home is boring.

NANCY. But the curfew.

PANNY. You're not home.

NANCY. I have a job.

PANNY. Oooh. You know, you used to be fun.

NANCY. I have responsibilities.

PANNY. You work at Walgreens, Nance.

NANCY. Sometimes I think you don't understand anything.

PANNY. Do you want me to wait till you get off work? We could hang out.

NANCY. Hang out? Hello, it's a school night.

PANNY. Yeah, I know, but. It'd be fun. Maybe we could go to Denny's.

NANCY. Denny's?

PANNY. Yeah, they do this thing where you get a free meal on your — forget it.

NANCY. Anyway, Will's picking me up.

PANNY. Oh. How's that going?

NANCY. Good. He's pretty cool.

PANNY. Yeah, he always seemed that way. I mean, just from history class he always seemed ... cool.

NANCY. Well, he is.

PANNY. Nance?

NANCY. What?

PANNY. Are you ... never mind.

NANCY. Just spit it out, what?

PANNY. You and Will haven't done it, right?

(She looks at Nancy, hard.)

Oh my God.

NANCY. What are you oh my God-ing for?

PANNY. You've only been going out for like, a month!

NANCY. A month is a long time. Can be a long time. I mean, do you realize there are insects whose entire life span is, like, three days?

PANNY. What does that have to do with anything?

NANCY. Time is relevant, okay? Things are different now.

PANNY. How?

NANCY. They just are. Could you stop looking at me like that?

PANNY. Like what?

NANCY. Like I'm a big slut all of a sudden.

PANNY. I wasn't.

NANCY. Because it's not a big deal.

PANNY. I think it kinda is. And you used to too.

NANCY. Well, that was before. This is now.

(Nancy goes back to stocking. Panny turns back to the magazine.)

PANNY. Look, it's that model we hate. She's everywhere. She's pretty, huh? Nance? *(She looks up. Nancy has left.)*

(Quietly.) I think she is.

(A man wanders on. He eyes the electronics on the shelf. Panny looks up and notices him and then goes back to her magazine. He looks around and then shoves a walkman into his jacket and bolts. She stands and watches him run out of the store. Nancy enters carrying a box.)

NANCY. What?

PANNY. I. There was.

NANCY. *(Annoyed.)* Yeah?

PANNY. Nothing.

Scene 3

The living room. Panny enters and goes straight for her room. Lefty enters from the kitchen.

LEFTY. Hey. Where were you?

PANNY. School. Why're you home?

LEFTY. Switched shifts.

PANNY. Why?

LEFTY. Someone asked me to.

PANNY. Is that the only reason? *(She looks at him carefully.)*

LEFTY. Yeah.

PANNY. Don't you know what day it is today? Don't you care?

LEFTY. Wednesday.

PANNY. No, it isn't just *Wednesday.* What kind of uncle are you?

LEFTY. Why're you shouting? Here. Something came for you.

PANNY. Really? *(He gives her a blue, airmail envelope.)* Oh.

LEFTY. Who's it from?

PANNY. No one. Something for school.

LEFTY. There's something else.

PANNY. I've got a lot of homework tonight, Lefty.

LEFTY. Two seconds.

PANNY. Fine.

LEFTY. I'll bring it here. *(He leaves. Panny starts to open the letter. He comes back bearing a beautiful cake with icing on it spelling out "Panny." There is a candle on it. He clears his throat. Panny jumps up when she sees the cake.)*

PANNY. Lefty! You jerk. You totally had me going.

LEFTY. I'm not singing so just hum it to yourself.

PANNY. Oh, it's, it's — You didn't have to, you really didn't.

LEFTY. Wish. *(Panny closes her eyes and makes a wish. She blows out the candle. Lefty takes the candle off the cake.)*

PANNY. Thank you. *(She hugs Lefty as Isabel walks in. She wears a ratty silk robe.)*

ISABEL. About time someone came home.

PANNY. Hey, Isabel.

ISABEL. How many times do I have to tell you? You're supposed to come home right away from school, right away.

PANNY. I'm sorry.

ISABEL. It's not like I'm being unreasonable, especially with the news full of — *(She notices the cake.)* Who brought this confection into my house?

LEFTY. I did.

ISABEL. Why, Lefty! What a lovely surprise! Why is it named Panny?

PANNY. It's *my* cake. Lefty brought it for me.

ISABEL. Well, let's not be greedy about it —

LEFTY. Isabel.

ISABEL. What?

LEFTY. It's her birthday, Isabel. *(A brief pause. It's clear this is entirely new information to Isabel but she doesn't even blink.)*

ISABEL. I know that, I'm her mother, don't you think I know that?

LEFTY. *(To Panny.)* Here. *(He takes out a tiny box from his shirt pocket.)*

PANNY. Sunmaid Raisins?

LEFTY. No. Was the only box I could find. The right size. *(Panny opens the box. She lifts out a pair of sparkly earrings dangling from a plastic square.)*

PANNY. *(A little taken aback.)* Oh. They're so — they're really really pretty. *(Isabel comes over and looks at the earrings.)*

ISABEL. You bought these?

LEFTY. Uh huh. *(To Panny.)* Do you like them? You don't like them.

PANNY. No, no, I do. Thank you. They're perfect. *(They hug.)*

ISABEL. Panny.

PANNY. What?

ISABEL. Come over here.

I have a gift for you too.

PANNY. You do?

LEFTY. You do?

ISABEL. Well, turning thirteen —

LEFTY. Fourteen —

ISABEL. Fourteen, it's a special occasion. You don't just turn fourteen every day. Someone, bring me The Yellow Pages. *(Pause.)* Today would be nice. *(Panny opens a cabinet and takes out The Yellow Pages. She hands it to Isabel. Isabel takes it and begins flipping through it.)* Of course, fourteen is not what it used to be. When I

13

was that age, I was already considered a woman. Nowadays, one begs the question: What is it to be a woman? It isn't enough to bleed, it isn't merely hormonal. It is not enough to be *d'un certain âge*, no. A girl becomes a woman, I believe, when she understands sacrifice for the first time.

PANNY. Sacrifice?

ISABEL. The world asks things of us constantly. It is never content with what we are; it asks us to dream of what we wish to be and then to have the courage to become that dream.

A woman is one who understands what the world asks of her, and answers with an eternal YES, an affirming YES. I say to you, Panny, now is the time to look at what the world asks of you and say YES, YES, YES! *(She spins the book towards Panny and points at an ad.)* This is my gift to you.

PANNY. I don't understand.

ISABEL. Plastic surgery.

Scene 4

PANNY. *Unheimlich.* That's what Freud called it when something familiar becomes a little strange. He says it's the familiarity which makes it disturbing. Like how the hallway of your house gets kind of scary at midnight when it no longer looks quite the same even though it is the same. Like your own reflection when you're not expecting it. Like clowns.

One day my mother came home looking as if she'd been hit in the face with a two by four. She stopped going to work; she just stayed home. And when the bandages finally came off, she was all healed and I guess she looked good. I mean, I guess she looked great. But when I saw her face for the first time, all I wanted to do was run away.

Unheimlich. Freud.

(Isabel's room. It is small, the main furniture being a television and an old easy chair. Isabel watches TV. Panny brings in a tray of food and sets it down.)

Isabel? I made mac and cheese.

ISABEL. Mnh. That poor girl. Did you know her?

PANNY. No. She was a senior.

ISABEL. They finally found her. Out by the reservoir. Pretty thing. They're running photos of her when she was part of the Homecoming Court. Well, she didn't stay pretty for long. Whoever did it didn't even bother digging a grave for the body. He just left it out there for the whole wide world to see. Disgraceful.

PANNY. Do they know who did it?

ISABEL. No. They thought it might be her boyfriend, but he's got an alibi. Not that that means anything. Most people are killed by someone they know.

Such a shame. All of them, blonde hair, blue eyes. So pretty. They could be sisters. Well, at least I don't have to worry about you.

PANNY. Uh huh.

ISABEL. So have you thought about it?

PANNY. About what?

ISABEL. About what you're going to have done?

PANNY. No.

ISABEL. Not even the — I mean, you don't even want to consider your — well, never mind.

PANNY. Consider my what?

ISABEL. No, you don't want it, that's fine. I'm not one to pressure anyone into anything.

PANNY. My what, Isabel?

ISABEL. Your nose.

PANNY. What's wrong with my nose?

ISABEL. Well, there's no bridge. I mean, pfft. Nothing.

PANNY. Do I need a bridge?

ISABEL. Okay, forget the nose. How about the eyes?

PANNY. What's wrong with my eyes?

ISABEL. Panny, let me tell you something. Look here: What do you see?

PANNY. Your nose.

ISABEL. But no! That's the genius of it! What you are seeing is actually part of my chin!

PANNY. No.

ISABEL. Yes! That's beauty! Take a little here, put it there and voilà! A perfect profile!

Panny, I too was a plain little girl with big yearnings. A diamond in the rough. And all I did was polish it a little. That's all this is: polish. Everyone does it. Every celebrity over the age of thirty-five. Everyone! I mean, I watch TV, I know.

Don't think of it as surgery. Think of it as a simple act of constructive self-improvement. I am challenging you, Panny. Everyone's always saying, boo hoo, beauty is so hard. Of course it's hard. Anything worthwhile is hard. True beauty is not born. True beauty is an act of will. And all you have to do is choose it, Panny. It's yours to choose.

Scene 5

PANNY. *Doppelganger.* A ghostly double of a living person, especially one that haunts its living counterpart. *Doppelganger. (Lights up on Hae-Yoon, a young Korean girl.)*
HAE-YOON. Dear Panny,
My name is Hae-Yoon, but if it make you happy, call me Elizabeth, because this is American name I' like. I like Elizabeth because it can change and be many things, like ME. It can be Liz or Beth or Eliza or Betty, which is GREAT because in Korean, Hae-Yoon is just Hae-Yoon.
I am very glad to be making your acquaintanceship. I think this program between your class and my class is GREAT because I have hope to improve my American English.
So a little about me.
I have long hair the color of Coca Cola and I drink Coca Cola every chance I can. My mother say this is why I am so short and have legs like radishes. But I think Coca Cola is GREAT!
I have many question for you.
One. Do you have boyfriend?
Two. Do you live near Hollywood?
Three. Do you have blond hairs?
Your pen pal,
Elizabeth.
P.S. I am waiting for your letter with much excitedment. I love mail. It is GREAT!
(Lights out on Hae-Yoon and up on Lefty. He is in the basement working on a large model of a battleground. There are miniatures of warriors scattered all over the model. Panny sits on a stool, writing on a notepad.)
PANNY. Okay. How does this sound:
Dear Elizabeth,

Dry up.
Sincerely,
Panny.

LEFTY. What's that?

PANNY. A letter to my pen pal.

LEFTY. Dry up?

PANNY. Too slang-y? She might not get it.

LEFTY. If you don't like her then why is she writing to you?

PANNY. It's our stupid project in homeroom. Apparently, my middle of nowhere, podunk school has a sister school in Asia. Go figure.

LEFTY. But that sounds nice.

PANNY. Yeah, like I want a chink pen pal —

LEFTY. Panny! Don't say that.

PANNY. What? Chink?

LEFTY. Yes.

PANNY. But it's true, I am a chink, you're a chink, Isabel's a —

LEFTY. But you don't say it. It's a bad word.

PANNY. If *other* people say it. But if I say it, it's like, you know, it's like black people saying —

LEFTY. PANNY.

PANNY. God. Since when does the First Amendment no longer work down here?

LEFTY. Where are you learning all this stuff?

PANNY. Chink? Get real, I've known that word since I was like five. *(She writes on her notepad.)*

Okay, how's this:

Dear Elizabeth,

Thank you for your letter. I am fascinated by your country too. I have a few questions for you as well:

Do you have indoor plumbing?

Do you eat dogs?

(She looks up.)

Oh, come on, Lefty. That was a joke.

LEFTY. That was not funny.

PANNY. I bet the kids in my homeroom would think it was funny.

LEFTY. Well, you're not like the kids in your homeroom.

(Pause.)

PANNY. No. You're right. I'm not. *(She crumples up the paper.)*

LEFTY. Something bothering you?

PANNY. No.

LEFTY. It wasn't a good birthday, was it?

PANNY. What?

LEFTY. You don't like the earrings, I can tell —

PANNY. Lefty, that's so not true —

LEFTY. You haven't worn them.

PANNY. I'm, I'm saving them for a special occasion.

LEFTY. You don't like them …

PANNY. Lefty. It's not that, it's … look. Look at me.
I don't have pierced ears. I never have.

LEFTY. Oh … why am I so …

PANNY. It's okay, Lefty. I mean, you're not the most observant guy in the world, but …

LEFTY. I mess up everything, I messed up your birthday, and then your mother with that crazy gift …

PANNY. You did not mess it up. And Isabel … I don't know … I guess in her own way, she was being thoughtful …

LEFTY. Thoughtful?

PANNY. Yeah …

LEFTY. Panny. Are you … don't tell me you're thinking about it?

PANNY. Well …

LEFTY. You don't need it. You're a very pretty girl.

PANNY. Oh, God. Here we go.

LEFTY. You are.

PANNY. Of course you think that; you're my uncle. You're, like, paid to say that.

LEFTY. Don't let her get to you.

PANNY. Look, if I want to think about it, so what? I mean, look at her, she looks great.

LEFTY. I thought you were more mature than this —

PANNY. Oh, like you should talk — *(She gestures to his miniatures.)* You call this mature, Mr. Dungeon Master?
I'm sorry … I didn't mean that.

LEFTY. You used to play it with me.

PANNY. Yeah, all I need is for it to get around that I play role-playing games to cement my reputation as the biggest geek in school.

LEFTY. You think I'm a geek.

PANNY. No, that's not what I meant. Look, I'm glad you have a hobby. God knows Isabel could use one. God knows *I* could use one.

LEFTY. I just want to see you happy.

PANNY. I know.

18

LEFTY. They say these are the best years of your life.
PANNY. Thanks. Now I feel much better.

Scene 6

*A department store jewelry counter. Lefty walks up. He is
wearing a security guard's uniform. Evvie is leaning on the
counter, reading a book.*

LEFTY. Hi, I need to — *(Evvie holds up her hand, signaling him to
shush. She finishes her chapter, closes the book and looks up.)*
EVVIE. Now. What may I help you with?
LEFTY. I need to return these. *(He puts the earrings on the counter.)*
EVVIE. Oh, great. The only sale tonight and it's a return. My
manager's going to love that.
LEFTY. She didn't like them, I mean, she doesn't have pierced ears.
EVVIE. Not too observant, are we?
LEFTY. You always read on the job?
EVVIE. What else is there to do? Time just draaaags on by. You
work here?
LEFTY. Yeah, upstairs.
EVVIE. Then you know what I mean. How boring it gets.
LEFTY. It's not so bad.
EVVIE. Please. No one even shoplifts anymore. I kind of miss it.
Miss the excitement. Like last year, there was this well-dressed couple
with a baby in a stroller, and they just stuffed that stroller with ties
and sweaters and shirts. They actually hid stuff *under* the baby. And I
bet it wasn't even their child.

Just shows you stealing's not about money. The people who
steal are hungry, but it's not for things. In fact, it's amazing more
people don't steal; these days everyone's hungry. Walking through
the mall, everyone looks sad, their mouths like this: *(She sets her
mouth in a grim line.)* People so well-dressed and so sad. We don't
know what we are, none of us.

Look at this. *(She gestures at her book.)* How to Make the Most of
Your Hidden Talent. Isn't that a marvelous title? Notice the phrasing.
It isn't *HOW TO DEVELOP a Hidden Talent.* No, it's *HOW TO*

19

MAKE THE MOST of it because it is already assuming you HAVE a talent. And you do. Everyone does. You and me, we have *talents!* Big ones. Inside us like cats have paws. You don't say much, do you?

LEFTY. What?

EVVIE. What do you think your talent is?

LEFTY. Your talent?

EVVIE. Well, according to the Chinese Zodiac, I am a rabbit, which means I am lucky, good with money, and articulate. I should be a lawyer or an actor. But then, considering I'm a Cancer, I'm also a homebody, who has the tendency to be emotional at times, and I'm a crab, see, so I don't go straight for things, I kind of scuttle at them, sideways like. I move towards what I want but indirectly. Which, I don't much like about myself, but there it is.

Of course my rising is Virgo, which means I like things a certain way — like you go to a party and some guest is emptying out the ashtrays and putting away the empty beer bottles, that's me. So all in all, adding it all up, I'd say my talent is ... color.

LEFTY. I'm sorry?

EVVIE. I am very, very good at seeing colors. Like you know how some people have perfect pitch? They can hear the gradations of pitches between notes, I mean, to the tiniest degree. And that's how I am with color.

Like that stack of sweaters over there: what does it look like to you?

LEFTY. A bunch of red sweaters.

EVVIE. I see that and I see variations in the dye, in how the light bounces off the folds of the fabric to produce many different reds, not just one. But what does this mean? What possible occupation does such a gift suggest? That, my friend, is the rub.

LEFTY. Maybe you could mix colors. Like paint colors.

EVVIE. They have computers that do that.

LEFTY. Interior decorate?

EVVIE. Just because I can see colors better, doesn't mean I know how to put them together. Like look at what I'm wearing. Does this seem to clash to you?

LEFTY. Maybe a little.

EVVIE. I know my talent. I just don't know where it goes.

Now you have got to have a talent. Everyone does.

LEFTY. I don't think so.

EVVIE. Must be something. Wait. Let me guess. I'm good at this. The Rabbit is very intuitive.

You … can … be extremely patient.

LEFTY. I can?

EVVIE. Because here it's been all this time and I haven't finished ringing up your return yet.

LEFTY. Oh.

EVVIE. Here. Just sign at the "x." *(He does. She hands him a copy of the receipt.)*

And there you go.

LEFTY. Guess I should go back upstairs.

EVVIE. Nice talking to you.

(He doesn't leave.)

LEFTY. I'm Lefty.

EVVIE. *(Points to her name badge.)* Evvie. Nice to meet you, Lefty.

LEFTY. If I have a talent, maybe it's my hands.

EVVIE. What can they do?

LEFTY. They can be very, very still.

And. Hold things. Carefully. So they don't break.

Is that a talent?

EVVIE. It sure is, baby. It sure is.

Scene 7

HAE-YOON. Dear Panny,

I appreciate very much the photo you send me of where you living. Wow! What a brown place! But what is this thing you write at the bottom of the photo … "BFE." You write that it means "Bum Fuck Egypt." Egypt I know, but what is a Bum Fuck?

Also, I didn't realize you were not full American. You are just another Asian person like me. I am a little disappoint but that is okay.

Here are answer to your question.

One, I would like to be teacher. Teach English. My idea is use lot of American movie to teach. And then I can have job to watch movie. Great!

Two, I have a mother who is very nice except she make me eat too much. My dad does not talk. He like to read paper every night on the floor even though we have a lot of chair. Korean people like floor better than chair.

Three, of course I know about plastic surgery. I have surgery when I was four. My mother take me to doctor and I go in and out. All my friend have eye surgery. Looks good! And all the movie and singing star also have surgery. My mother say we are lucky that it is so easy to be pretty. During the war, she say, no one was pretty. Now she want me to do something about my radish leg. There is surgery for making leg thinner. They cut out the thick part, below knee. She say it won't hurt.

Four, my favorite food is melon gum. I am sending you a stick of this gum with my letter. It is GREAT!

Your pen pal,
Elizabeth.

Scene 8

Panny lies on her bed, staring at the ceiling. She reaches for her phone and dials. Lights up on Hugo.

HUGO. Hello?

PANNY. Hi, is Nancy there?

HUGO. Who's Nancy?

PANNY. Her mom gave me this number?

HUGO. *(Mimicking her intonation.)* Why do you make a statement as if it's a question?

PANNY. You're making fun of me?

HUGO. Oh, come on? Have a sense of — *(She hangs up.)*
     Okay, don't.

(Panny calls again.)
     Hello?

PANNY. Oh, shoot.

HUGO. You know, dialing's not that hard.

PANNY. Why are you so obnoxious?

HUGO. Moi? *(Panny hangs up. Hugo dials. The phone rings.)*

PANNY. Hello?

HUGO. I am not obnoxious.

PANNY. How'd you do that?

HUGO. I'm psychic. It's called Caller ID. Hmmm. There's no description. You sound cute. Are you? *(Panny hangs up. Hugo dials.*

The phone rings. Panny hesitantly picks it up.)

Don't hang up.

PANNY. I'm sorry, I think you have the wrong number —

HUGO. I have a question for you.

PANNY. Listen, I don't know who you're —

HUGO. Question. Would you rather have dark, curly hair all over your body OR would you rather have a small, curly tail that no one can see?

Hello? Not good, huh?

Okay, how about: Would you rather sneeze cottage cheese or cry vegetable oil?

You're being quiet. Does this mean you're not going to hang up?

I am very bored. If you do not talk to me I will be forced to watch some rather unpalatable television.

Okay, easier question. Would you rather talk to me on the phone or would you rather I hang up? *(Pause.)*

PANNY. I would rather … talk on the phone.

HUGO. Well, peachy. So would I.

PANNY. *(To us:)* And that's how I met Hugo.

(Time has passed. Panny and Hugo are on the phone. Hugo's reading out of a huge textbook.)

HUGO. This is my favorite: trichotillomania. That's when you obsessively pluck hair from your head and then you eat it.

PANNY. Gross.

HUGO. I love this stuff.

PANNY. This is homework?

HUGO. For psych class.

PANNY. Psych? What kind of class is that?

HUGO. I don't know … a social science class?

PANNY. … Where do you go to school?

HUGO. Southwest Community.

PANNY. That's college.

HUGO. Duh.

PANNY. How old are you?

HUGO. Twenty. Took some time off after high school, so I started late. How about you?

PANNY. I'm … eighteen.

HUGO. Where d'you go?

PANNY. Brimsdale. High school.

HUGO. No kidding, I went to O'Connor. You figure out what you're going to do after you graduate?

PANNY. I don't know, move?

HUGO. Why? It's so beautiful here.

PANNY. Are you kidding me?

HUGO. You don't think so?

PANNY. No.

HUGO. Come on, the sunsets? The mountains?

PANNY. I guess.

HUGO. You should take some time and really look at it, Panny. It's like that French saying, "*Si vous prenez mes yeux, vous les trouverez beaux.*"

PANNY. Wow.

HUGO. Means, "If you look into my eyes, you will find them beautiful."

PANNY. Where'd you learn French like that? In France?

HUGO. No … in French class.

PANNY. Right. So what did you do after you graduated?

HUGO. I went on my mission.

PANNY. Your what?

HUGO. My mission.

PANNY. Like a superhero?

HUGO. No. Like a Mormon.

PANNY. You're Mormon?

HUGO. Why do you say it like that?

PANNY. 'Cause you seem kind of normal is all.

HUGO. Gee. Thanks.

PANNY. No, I just meant. Mormon. So then you can't swear or anything.

HUGO. Nope.

PANNY. So what do you do when you get really mad?

HUGO. I don't know. I don't remember the last time I got mad.

PANNY. Really?

HUGO. Stuff just doesn't bother me.

PANNY. Because of your religion?

HUGO. No, because of my personality.

PANNY. So where did they send you? For your mission? Like deepest Africa?

HUGO. No. Baltimore.

PANNY. What kind of missionary goes to Baltimore?

HUGO. Hey, people in Baltimore are just as needy.

PANNY. For what? Polygamy?

HUGO. Panny, we don't do that anymore.

PANNY. No?

HUGO. No, the crazy ones out in the sticks, the fundamentalists, they do it.

PANNY. Oh, so the normal Mormons, you guys just own Pepsi.

HUGO. Ha ha.

PANNY. So your father has only one wife? You didn't grow up in a compound?

HUGO. No. Anyway, my dad's dead.

PANNY. Oh. God. I'm sorry.

HUGO. Don't be. Happened a long time ago.

PANNY. I don't really have a father either.

HUGO. Did he — ?

PANNY. No, he's alive. At least, I think he is. He and my mom never got married. She got pregnant with me by accident. He took off.

HUGO. He couldn't handle it?

PANNY. I don't know. No one ever says. *(Pause.)*

HUGO. Hey. Tell me something you've never told anyone before.

PANNY. What?

HUGO. Tell me something you've never told anyone else before.

PANNY. Why?

HUGO. Because I want to hear it.

PANNY. Okay … I … Like what kind of thing?

HUGO. Any kind of thing.

PANNY. Okay. Um.

There was this one time. I was sitting here, at my desk. It was really late and I only had my desk lamp on. I was stretching or something and happened to catch my reflection in the window. And I don't know — the quality of the light or something — but it was like for this really brief moment, I wasn't me. I actually seemed … beautiful. I'm only saying that because, see, in reality, I'm not. I'm not beautiful. At all. But it was like because it was so late and there was absolutely no one around, I was beautiful — a little. And I thought, oh, it's like my beautiful self is this imaginary friend, my inner Snuffalupagus that only I can see.

I don't know. That was stupid. You tell me something, okay? Something you've never said to anyone.

HUGO. There's nothing. I've said everything.

PANNY. No secrets?

HUGO. None.

PANNY. Come on.

HUGO. Something I've never said to anyone …

Okay.

I've never liked anyone's voice half as much as I like yours.

PANNY. Really?

HUGO. Really.

Scene 9

Isabel's room. Panny enters with a tray of food and sets it down.

ISABEL. I'm starved. Watching the news is so exhausting.

PANNY. Did they find him yet?

ISABEL. Nope. They're starting to call in psychics. God, I wish I were psychic! Just imagine: it'd be the perfect job. You could do it from home, get paid by the hour, never even leave your bed. *(Panny looks at the TV.)*

PANNY. This isn't the news.

ISABEL. News isn't back on till ten.

PANNY. What is this?

ISABEL. A five-part series on World War II.

PANNY. You're kidding.

ISABEL. Panny, I am not some Philistine. I like to learn. Besides, I think that General MacArthur is quite good-looking. They broke the mold when they made him. If he was on this case, he'd have that killer like that.

PANNY. Whatever.

ISABEL. Where're you going?

PANNY. I've got stuff to do. *(Panny leaves. Isabel looks at her food sadly.)*

ISABEL. *(Sighing.)* Nothing but war rations. *(The opening strains of the theme to a soap opera. The General appears. He is dressed in jodhpurs and aviator sunglasses. He's very dashing.)*

GENERAL. Isabel, my love.

ISABEL. Darling! You've come back.

GENERAL. Just as I promised. But now I must go again.

ISABEL. But it's been so difficult without you!

GENERAL. Someday, my dear, you will have nothing but the finest steak and caviar.

ISABEL. Don't tell me you have to go — I can't bear it.

GENERAL. But you must.

ISABEL. Tell me again how I looked the first time you saw me.

GENERAL. Flawless, you were flawless. And I knew you were beautiful, not because of the eyes of the men who watched you, their eyes filled with desire. But because of the eyes of the women who watched you, their eyes filled with envy. *(He puts on a pair of white gloves.)*

I must go lead my men, the men who are everywhere dying in islands all over the Pacific, dying for the great cause.

ISABEL. God, your courage! The magnificence of your spirit!

GENERAL. Greatness is such a burden.

ISABEL. I'll wait for you. *(He takes her in his arms and kisses her.)*

GENERAL. I shall return! *(He sweeps offstage.)*

ISABEL. Conquer the world and lay it at my feet! *(The music fades.)*

Conquer the world and give it to me as a token of love.

Scene 10

The department store. Evvie reads aloud from a book.

EVVIE. "Each of us is born with a remarkable talent that is unique. The key to a happy and successful personal and professional life is utilizing the remarkable talents we are born with."

Oooh, there's a test. Let's take it, we're going to take it, okay? You with me?

LEFTY. Not good at tests.

EVVIE. It's not that kind of test! One: When faced with a new situation, do you feel a) challenged, b) hesitant — *(Lefty takes out a miniature from his breast pocket and puts it on Evvie's book.)*

What's this?

LEFTY. You like it?

EVVIE. But where'd it come from?

LEFTY. They're part of a game that people play all over the world. There are stores, you go and you paint your pieces and then you play with them against other people. At the store.

EVVIE. Is it a toy?

LEFTY. No. It's hard to explain. There are competitions for painting these miniatures, judged on originality and artistry. The winner receives the Golden Blade, which is an actual sword. And then the winner is famous — among the other players. Miniatures by a Golden Blade winner can go for upwards of five hundred dollars.

EVVIE. Did you paint this?

LEFTY. Uh huh. It's part of a whole world, see, and you create different figures, outfitting them with weapons that you create or modify. There are all these different orders of wizards and warriors and — *(He stops, self-conscious.)*

EVVIE. Go on.

LEFTY. It's just a hobby. Nevermind. *(He tries to take the figure from Evvie but she holds it away from him.)*

EVVIE. The colors. You mixed these?

LEFTY. Yes.

EVVIE. How did you get into the small spaces?

LEFTY. Some of the brushes I use are only a few hairs large.

EVVIE. And you can see that?

LEFTY. Sometimes I use a magnifying glass.

EVVIE. You know, there are two things that seem miraculous and two things only. The very big and the very small. And our problem, Lefty, is that we are neither.

What does this one do?

LEFTY. She's a healer.

EVVIE. Can I keep her?

LEFTY. I made it for you.

Scene 11

Hugo and Panny are on their respective phones. Panny is lying on her bed. Hugo is stretched out on a couch.

HUGO. Pretend. Where are you?

PANNY. In my room.

HUGO. Okay, I'm walking in the door. What do I see?

PANNY. On your right, my closet. It's mirrored. You have to kick some clothes out of your way. Kind of a mess. And then you see me, lying on my bed, against the wall. *(Hugo moves from the couch to Panny's bed.)*

HUGO. I'm moving to my bed too. Which side are you on?

PANNY. Kind of in the center.

HUGO. Scoot over, you bed hog.

PANNY. I'm on the right now. Against the wall. My back is turned to you.

HUGO. Okay, I'm on the left then. My back's to you too. Can you feel me?

PANNY. Yes. *(The two are lying down on Panny's bed, turned away from each other.)*

I can feel the heat from you.

HUGO. I'm always warm.

PANNY. My hands and feet are always cold. Poor circulation.

HUGO. Warm them on me. Are you? Good.

(A moment.)

So ... when are we going to meet?

PANNY. Hugo ...

HUGO. I'm good all this week.

PANNY. I told you.

HUGO. I know, I know. Still not ready.

(Pause.)

PANNY. I hear that Mormons believe that the more souls you save, the better your chances of getting into heaven. That's why you do all that mission stuff.

HUGO. Yeah, I guess the hardcore ones believe that.

PANNY. And the hardcore ones believe if you're not white, you don't get into as good a heaven. Like there are these different levels.

HUGO. Where'd you learn all this?

PANNY. I looked it up. Internet.

HUGO. I see.

PANNY. Is it true?

HUGO. Truth is like most things. Depends on which way you approach it.

PANNY. I don't think I look like what you think I look like.

HUGO. Okay, I think I understood that.

PANNY. You're going to be disappointed.

HUGO. How could I be? It'll be you.

PANNY. You say that now.

HUGO. I won't change.

PANNY. Do you care about me?

HUGO. You know.

It's kind of funny.

But I do. I really do.

I don't even know why. I hardly know you, never even seen you. But I think you have a good heart. And I think you are full of dreams. I want you, whatever happiness you've had in your life up to this point, I want you to have it a thousandfold. And every sadness you have, or ever had, or ever will have, I wish I could take it from you. Does that make sense?

Panny.

Panny?

PANNY. I need to go.

HUGO. Did I say something?

PANNY. No. I just. My uncle's home. I need to eat dinner. Call me tomorrow, okay?

HUGO. Okay.

PANNY. Good night.

HUGO. Good night, Panny. Have some beautiful dreams. *(They hang up. Hugo stands up and walks off. Panny lies alone on her bed.)*

Scene 12

The mall food court. Lefty and Evvie are seated at a small, plastic table.

EVVIE. What was that? I can't quite hear you. There seems to be some kind of acoustic black hole right above our heads.

LEFTY. I said: Oh, never mind.

EVVIE. How long you been working for the store?

LEFTY. Nine, ten years.

EVVIE. Don't you get sick of mall food?

LEFTY. No.

EVVIE. That tie looks nice on you. I'll put it back on the display at the end of the night.

LEFTY. Thanks.

EVVIE. Do you think I look nice?

LEFTY. Yes. You look very nice.

EVVIE. Because you know that's what you do. On a date. You tell your date she looks nice.

LEFTY. You do. Look nice.

EVVIE. Maybe this wasn't a good idea. Maybe we're better off being friends. Because we are friends, aren't we?

LEFTY. This is a date?

EVVIE. Isn't it?

LEFTY. I don't really know. It's been so long.

EVVIE. Suddenly I'm nervous. Say the word, "date," and I'm nervous.

LEFTY. Am I making you nervous?

EVVIE. Not you. The idea. I haven't been on a date in. God. At least ten years. Between raising Jess and working, it just didn't seem like time ... Oh. The books say not to do that. Talk about kids on the first date. The books say not to show all your cards — baggage is what they really mean.

LEFTY. I don't care about that stuff. Make you feel any better, here: I'm a grown man and I still live with my sister and her teenage daughter.

EVVIE. Well, I'm forty and a single mother.

LEFTY. In my spare time, I play a role-playing game whose main audience is thirteen-year-old, pimply-faced boys.

EVVIE. I haven't had sex in eleven years. *(She laughs. It's a really nice laugh.)*

Like that old Woody Allen joke: I haven't had sex in eleven years — twenty counting my marriage. Baddum bum chh.

LEFTY. You're not like any black woman I know.

EVVIE. What's that supposed to mean?

LEFTY. Because you like Woody Allen. And because you like me.

EVVIE. Oh, now.

Lefty?

LEFTY. Uh huh.

EVVIE. Who were you buying them earrings for?

LEFTY. My neice. She just turned fourteen.

EVVIE. Ah. Yes.

(Pause.)

LEFTY.	EVVIE.
What are you doing after work?	So I'm free after work.

(Pause. Evvie laughs.)

EVVIE. I can see auras too, did I tell you that?

LEFTY. No. *(She looks at him and squints her eyes.)*

EVVIE. Blue, like ocean. All around your head.

Scene 13

The living room. The front door opens. Lefty enters.

ISABEL. Hello? Lefty? That you? *(She enters the living room. Lefty gets out The Yellow Pages and looks up a number.)*
 Where have you been?
 What, you don't even say hello anymore?
LEFTY. Hello. *(He finds what he's looking for and dials. Into the phone:)* One large pepperoni. Uh huh. 241-9033. Yes. Thank you. *(He hangs up.)*
ISABEL. What was that?
LEFTY. Dinner.
ISABEL. Marvelous! I'm absolutely famished. *(Lefty leaves the room.)*
 We haven't had dinner all together in ages.
 (Calling.) How was work today?
LEFTY. *(Offstage.)* Fine.
ISABEL. They still haven't found the man who did it.
LEFTY. Did what?
ISABEL. Doesn't anybody in this house watch the news? *(He enters wearing nice pants and buttoning up a new shirt. He throws his uniform over a chair.)*
LEFTY. Here's money.
ISABEL. You look nice. Is that new?
LEFTY. From the men's department.
ISABEL. What's that smell?
LEFTY. Oh, you know how those fragrance people are, spray you as soon as you get near them. Smell okay?
ISABEL. Yes.
LEFTY. There's soda in the fridge.
ISABEL. Where are you going?
LEFTY. I'm going out with some friends from work.
ISABEL. What friends?
LEFTY. Just friends.
ISABEL. But I thought, I thought we were going to have dinner together.
LEFTY. Next time.

ISABEL. Why not tonight?

LEFTY. I already made plans ...

ISABEL. So break them. We're your *family*, Lefty.

LEFTY. I know that.

ISABEL. I'm just saying there are certain duties that come with —

LEFTY. You don't have to tell me what my *duty* is, Isabel. Don't I sit in that stupid department store and do it every day?

ISABEL. Since when do you dislike your job?

LEFTY. I don't, I just ...

ISABEL. Lefty, what more could you want than this? A home. A family. All the things we wanted so much — we have them. Everything we want: It's already ours.

LEFTY. I don't know ... it is, but it's *not*.

ISABEL. Who's putting these ideas in your head? Your "friends"? I'm sure they're perfectly nice, but it has *always* been just you and me, Lefty, and you know what? It will always *be* just you and me.

LEFTY. I know you've always *said* that —

ISABEL. Because it's true.

LEFTY. You don't know that.

ISABEL. What's that supposed to mean?

LEFTY. Nothing. I have to go.

ISABEL. I am not done with you yet —

LEFTY. *Yes you are.*

(Pause.)

I have to go.

Don't wait up. *(He leaves.)*

ISABEL. Lefty?

LEFTY. *(She opens the door. She stands at the threshold. She can't bring herself to step outside. She shuts the door. She picks up Lefty's uniform. She looks through the pockets. She finds a slim paperback book.)*

(Reading.) How to Start Living. For Yourself.

Scene 14

Panny and Hugo are on the phone.

HUGO. I think it's time.
PANNY. For what?
HUGO. To meet.
PANNY. Hugo …
HUGO. Don't worry. It'll be okay.
PANNY. You don't know that …
HUGO. Trust me.
PANNY. I do.
HUGO. Then?
PANNY. Look, I don't have a car, how could I meet you?
HUGO. I could come over.
PANNY. No — I don't like having people over. My family.
HUGO. Then I'll pick you up. We'll go for a drive. Take you anywhere you want. Or just sit in your driveway.
PANNY. I can't, not tonight.
HUGO. Then let's meet in the morning, before school, or after school, I don't care.
PANNY. *(Panicking.)* I can't meet you.
HUGO. Tomorrow's bad? Okay, then how about —
PANNY. NO. It's not tomorrow, or the next day, it's — I can't, Hugo, I just can't.
HUGO. I don't understand.
PANNY. We can't meet.
HUGO. But I thought we were — I mean, I thought you wanted to —
PANNY. No. I don't.
HUGO. I see.
PANNY. Hugo, it's, it's complicated.
HUGO. I guess so.
PANNY. I just need time.
HUGO. How much time? Six months? A year?
    What are you afraid of? *(Pause.)*
    What's near you, a park? A store? Something within walking

distance.

PANNY. I don't know, there's a, there's a Walgreens ...

HUGO. The one on Greenfield?

PANNY. Yeah, but —

HUGO. I'll be there in an hour.

PANNY. What? Hugo ...

HUGO. Look, it's up to you. But I'll be there. Just think it over, okay?

PANNY. I don't know.

HUGO. In an hour. If you're there, you're there. If you're not ... you're not.

Scene 15

Isabel is in her room. Panny is in the bathroom. She sits on the counter with her feet in the sink. She looks at herself in the mirror. She pulls out a fashion magazine and flips it open.

ISABEL. When I was just a little girl, I asked my mother what would I be and she said, if I were lucky, I would be a housewife just like her. Well. I said to her, I don't think so. Just like that. *I don't think so.*

PANNY. *(Reading.)* Don't line the inside of your eyelid. Not only is it possible to injure and infect the eye, it will make your eyes look smaller.

ISABEL. I knew what I would be. I would not be my mother. I would be what I have always wanted to be: a fascinating woman.

PANNY. Apply the eyeshadow under the crease of your eyelid ... crease ... of your eyelid. *(Panny looks at herself and realizes she has no crease.)*

Okay, skip it.

ISABEL. At the age of seven, I remember going to sleep at night, and on my nightstand I had a notebook. In this notebook, I had written reminders to myself on *How to be a Fascinating Woman.* One: Speak quietly.

PANNY. Use a lip pencil to keep your lipstick from bleeding.

ISABEL. Two: Listen well.

35

PANNY. Use loose powder to control shine.

ISABEL. Three: Smile without showing teeth.

PANNY. Apply blush in an upwards, sweeping motion.

ISABEL. And four:

Always, always pause in the doorway before entering a room. *(She holds a pose briefly, as if she is leaning against the doorframe like a silent movie star. Panny strikes a pose vaguely similar to Isabel's. She has succeeded in applying a lot of make-up to her face. She doesn't exactly look older but she does look very different.)*

PANNY. On your way to the new you.

ISABEL. A fascinating woman indeed.

(Panny turns out the light. Strains of Isabel's soap opera music begin. The General appears.)

GENERAL. I've gotten your packages, my darling, gotten them all. I'm the best-dressed man on the battlefield.

ISABEL. When will we go to DeeCee?

GENERAL. Soon, my dear, soon.

ISABEL. I'm being patient.

GENERAL. Yes, you are, and I love you for it.

ISABEL. You do?

GENERAL. You know what you are? You're my empress. My queen. My — *(The doorbell rings. The General disappears. It takes Isabel a moment to realize what the sound is. There is now an insistent knocking at the door. Isabel finally goes to the door and opens it. There stands Jack, a pizza delivery guy in a slouchy uniform.)*

JACK. Hey. You order a pizza?

Ma'am?

Is this the right place?

(Isabel stares at him. She breaks out into a slow smile.)

ISABEL. Why, yes. Yes, it is.

Scene 16

Evvie's place.

EVVIE. You okay?

LEFTY. I like this place. It feels like you.

It's funny not knowing where anything is.

EVVIE. Well, it's pretty easy. Bathroom. Hall. Bedrooms back there. Kitchen. See? Nothing to it. *(Lefty looks at a framed photo.)*

LEFTY. Is that her? Jess? She's cute.

EVVIE. Yeah, she was. Till she became a teenager. Then it was just fight fight fight.

LEFTY. And now she's in college?

EVVIE. Yeah. You know, if she still lived here, you could stand here and hear her breathing. And she could hear us talking, the walls are that thin. It's funny. Sometimes it feels like I never had a child. And all this time it was like I wanted to be something for her and now I have to learn to be something for myself.

LEFTY. Why'd you and your husband get a divorce?

EVVIE. I don't know. He cheated on me and we tried to work it out. Stay together, you know, for Jess. And it seemed okay, for awhile. I mean, not great, but not awful. Then somehow, I got on this self-help kick. I mean those books are everywhere and I just picked one up one day. It was called: *How to Get Rid of the Clutter in Your Life.* I had this real bad habit, couldn't throw nothing away. This book was real helpful. It had like this test. You took every object you owned and took a hard look at it and asked yourself three things. One: Is it useful? Two: Does it make me happy? Three: Do I really, really love it?

So I'm sitting there, looking at the things in my living room and then my eyes just kind of straaay over and land on my husband. And I think to myself: Is it useful? Does it make me happy? Do I really, really love it?

I started divorce proceedings the next day.

LEFTY. Wow.

EVVIE. I tell you, those books changed my life.

Did you ever come close to getting married?

LEFTY. No.

EVVIE. Why not?

LEFTY. I don't know … by the time I thought about it, I already had a family to take care of. My sister got pregnant. And the dad didn't stick around. So I did.

EVVIE. It's a wonder she kept it. A lot of girls don't.

LEFTY. Yeah, but it was different for her. For us. See, we were adopted, my sister and me. Don't know anything about our birth parents except that they didn't want us. And the family that raised us sure didn't know what to make of us. Lots of times it felt like we just gave birth to ourselves. And I didn't want her kid to grow up like that. Always feeling … wrong. Like you've put on someone else's glasses, or sat in the wrong seat. No.

EVVIE. You wanted something better for her.

LEFTY. Yes. And Panny is my child. I mean, I think of her like my own.

EVVIE. Of course you do. *(Pause.)*

LEFTY. Evvie?

EVVIE. Yeah?

LEFTY. You make me feel like I'm in the right seat.

(She smiles.)

EVVIE. Would you like to see my aura?

LEFTY. I can't.

EVVIE. Sure you can.

LEFTY. I don't have the gift.

EVVIE. Yeah, you do. You just don't know it. We all start off with these abilities — children are great at seeing auras — but then, as we become adults, we tune out, we simplify, we become linear. And that's how the world loses some of its magic.

Here. Rub your hands together. Real fast. Just do it. Till they're nice and hot. *(Lefty does.)*

Now shake them. Now bring your hands together — slowly. You feel it? Like this fuzzy ball between your hands? You're feeling the aura of one hand bumping up against the aura of the other hand. Now, come here. Put your hand over me. *(Lefty slowly moves his hand over Evvie's body, about four inches away.)*

That's what you'd call scanning my aura. Feel it?

Now look at me. Look at my forehead. Relax. In your peripheral vision, there should be a kind of fuzz extending out from my body. You see it?

LEFTY. It's just my eyes blurring —

EVVIE. Don't be skeptical. That's rule one. Okay. You should have some sense that something's there, you just don't know what. Don't give up, just keep looking. Don't look in my *eyes*, Lefty, you're not supposed to look *at* me —

LEFTY. I love you.

EVVIE. What?

LEFTY. I love you. I'm going to go home. And I'm going to get my things and come back here. I want to be with you. Will you let me be with you?

EVVIE. Yes.

Scene 17

PANNY. *(To us:)* Between me and the Walgreens on Greenfield is a long grove of orange trees. It's a short drive but a long walk. A nice walk. The trees bring the temperature down so it's cool. And there's hardly any traffic. The line dividing the street is like a perforation, like if you tugged on the street, it'd rip down that broken line all the way to the horizon.

And there's nothing but the wind moving through the trees. It's a beautiful sound, I never heard anything so beautiful. Like the wind could cleanse you.

I'm walking along that road and then I hear a long, low whoosh. And for the briefest moment, I can't tell if it's the sound of the wind or the rush of an oncoming car.

(In front of the Walgreens. Panny arrives, out of breath and nervous. There's a water machine and a bike rack. The lighting is fluorescent and stark. Panny tries to find a nonchalant pose. Hugo enters. Panny freezes, watching him. Hugo sees her but doesn't really pay any attention to her. He looks off, down the sidewalk leading to the drugstore. A man enters and puts an empty bottle into the water machine. The man begins putting quarters into the machine. There's the loud sound of water hitting the bottom of the bottle just as Panny says:)

Hugo? *(Hugo doesn't hear her. The man keeps filling the water. The doors of the drugstore open and Nancy walks out.)*

NANCY. Hey. What're you doing here?

PANNY. Oh, hi, Nance. Just needed a few things.

NANCY. What's up?

PANNY. Good. I mean, nothing much. You?

NANCY. Same. Nothing much. *(Notices Panny's face.)* Are you wearing — ?

PANNY. So, you going home?

NANCY. Yeah, I'm all cramp-y, so my manager's letting me off early.

PANNY. Is Will picking you up?

NANCY. Will and I broke up.

PANNY. You're kidding.

NANCY. Whatever. I was getting sick of him anyway.

PANNY. I'm sorry.

NANCY. Like I said, whatever.

Shit. Is that — ?

Hugo?

Hey. Hugo. It's me — Lisa's friend.

HUGO. Oh, hey. What's up?

NANCY. Nothing. What're you doing down here?

HUGO. Meeting a friend. You?

NANCY. I work here. Oh, this is my friend —

PANNY. Hi. We go to school together. Me and Nancy. *(She sticks out her hand. Hugo doesn't notice.)*

HUGO. Is that so? *(Hugo goes back to the edge of the stage, looking off.)*

NANCY. *(Calling.)* Is he late?

HUGO. What?

NANCY. Whoever you're meeting.

HUGO. Kind of.

NANCY. Well, if you want to give up and go home, I could use a ride.

HUGO. What time do you got?

NANCY. Quarter after.

HUGO. Was there anyone else here? Before?

NANCY. I don't know. *(Turns to Panny.)* Was there?

PANNY. No.

NANCY. Nope.

So what do you say?

I really, really could use a ride.

HUGO. Yeah ... okay. All right. *(He gives one last long look down the street.)*

Come on. *(Nancy turns to Panny and gives her some kind of excited gesture that basically means: score!)*

NANCY. See ya later, Panny. *(Nancy leaves. Hugo freezes. He turns around. Panny turns her face away from him.)*

HUGO. Panny? *(Panny slowly nods without looking at him.)*

How old are you.

PANNY. Fourteen.

HUGO. Fourteen. *(Hugo starts to laugh. It isn't a pleasant laugh.)*

PANNY. Hugo, I —

HUGO. Good one.

You got me.

You really did. *(Hugo leaves.)*

PANNY. Hugo, wait — let me explain. *Hugo. (Panny stares after him, unable to believe he's really gone. Beat.)*

MAN. It's cheaper here.

PANNY. What?

MAN. Over at the Smith's, they rip you off. A quarter a gallon. Here it's only fifteen cents. *(Pause.)* Why you got all that stuff on your face?

PANNY. What?

MAN. Pretty girl like you, doesn't need all that stuff. *(Panny starts to cry.)*

Oh, no, hon, what is it? What'd I say? Don't cry, sweetheart. Here. *(He gives her a handkerchief from his pocket.)*

Go on, it's clean. I don't care, you can just get your snot all over it. Make you feel better. Get it all out. *(Panny laughs a little even as she's crying.)*

PANNY. I'm sorry …

MAN. For what? Life's tough. Especially at your age. So go ahead, have a good cry.

PANNY. I just feel so stupid.

MAN. We all do from time to time. Say the wrong thing, do the wrong thing.

It's hard. Living is hard.

There. Feel better?

PANNY. Yes. Thank you. *(She hands him back the handkerchief.)*

MAN. No, go ahead, keep it. It's yours.

PANNY. Thank you.

MAN. Don't mention it. *(He gets up and goes back to the water machine. His bottle is done filling. He caps it and pulls it out of the machine. It falls to the ground.)*

Damn.

PANNY. Are you okay?

MAN. Yeah. Say, I don't suppose you'd mind helping me out a sec? It's just I threw my back out pretty recently. Never thought it'd happen to me, thought back trouble was for old people, you know?

PANNY. Yeah.

MAN. But some help, that'd be great.

PANNY. Sure.

MAN. Car's right over there. *(He goes offstage. Panny faces front.)*

PANNY. *(To us:)* Later I realized that I had seen him before. *(We are back to the scene at the drugstore at the beginning. Briefly, we see the man in front of a shelf. He steals the walkman just as before. He runs out as Panny stands and watches him. To us:)* But I didn't remember this in time. *(Lights come back on the Man.)*

MAN. Hey, you okay?

PANNY. Yeah.

MAN. Well, I sure appreciate the help.

PANNY. No problem. *(She picks up one end of the water bottle. They go.)*

Scene 18

The living room. Isabel is looking through a purse as if she's looking for money. Jack is waiting.

ISABEL. It was right here. Don't know where it's gone.

JACK. It's sixteen eighty-two with tax.

ISABEL. Now if I were a wallet, where would I be? You look thirsty. Where are my manners? May I offer you a libation?

JACK. A what?

ISABEL. A soda? A beer?

JACK. I don't think so, I've got two more deliveries to make —

ISABEL. But just while you wait.

JACK. Isn't that a twenty on the table?

ISABEL. Well, look at that! How did that get there?

JACK. I've got change. *(He reaches for the bill but Isabel pockets it.)*

ISABEL. Why be in such a rush? Have a seat. You've got that padded thing, it'll keep the pizzas warm. Wouldn't you like a little break?

JACK. Well, it has been a busy night —

ISABEL. There. Sit. *(She turns on a tape player. The sound of a song like Elvis' "It's Now or Never" comes on.* She gets out a bottle of wine and two glasses.)* Now. Why don't we just have a nice drink.

JACK. I don't know …

ISABEL. It's just a tiny, little glass! A light refreshment.

JACK. I'm driving.

ISABEL. *(She leans forward and reads his nametag.)* Jack. Relax. Just have a sip. *(She hands him a glass, toasts it with him, and then downs it in one long swallow.)* Feel it. Feel how hot my face is. *(She puts his hand to her face.)*

You have. Nice hands.

* See Special Note on Songs and Recordings on copyright page.

JACK. I do? *(She runs her hand along his shoulder.)*
ISABEL. And a beautiful uniform.
JACK. It came with the job.
(She presses her cheek to his chest.)
ISABEL. Smells like … war. And faraway places. And power — you command men, yes?
JACK. Um, I'm just a driver.
ISABEL. I love a modest man. *(She begins caressing him. Jack doesn't know what to do, but he doesn't particularly wish to stop it.)*
    Do you think I'm beautiful?
JACK. What?
ISABEL. Yes or no. Just answer.
JACK. Well, yeah, I guess you're hot but I don't —
ISABEL. Then kiss me.
JACK. What?
ISABEL. I've been waiting for you, General. All this time. Only for you. *(She leans in to kiss him. Jack jumps up.)*
JACK. Whoa whoa whoa.
ISABEL. What is it? What's wrong? *(She turns off the music.)*
JACK. Is this some kind of joke?
ISABEL. What?
JACK. Let me guess, guys at the parlor, they put you up to this, right? *(He walks around the room.)* Where is it, huh?
ISABEL. Where is what?
JACK. Some kind of hidden camera. *(He looks around.)*
ISABEL. Jack — it's Jack, right? There's no one here but us.
JACK. Yeah, you expect me to believe that you're some hot lonely woman who has a thing for pizza delivery guys. Who put you up to this?
ISABEL. No one put me up to anything.
JACK. Yeah, right — where'd they find you? Back of *The New Times?*
ISABEL. I'm sorry — ?
JACK. They're such assholes, God! Always setting me up, trying to make me look like an idiot. But this — paying some woman to jerk me around —
ISABEL. You think I'm some kind of prostitute?
JACK. Oh, come on. Look at you. Could you wear any more make-up?
ISABEL. I … look … like a prostitute?
JACK. Well … aren't you?

43

(Silence.)

Oh ... oh, shit.

Ma'am? Ma'am, listen to me —

ISABEL. Ma'am? You think I'm old too!

JACK. NO, no, you don't look old, you look great. Miss ... Miss. I am so sorry. I thought ... I just assumed ... So this is for real?

ISABEL. It *was.*

JACK. Oh ... God ... I am so, I am SO sorry.

ISABEL. Stay away from me.

JACK. Listen, can you blame me? This kind of stuff doesn't happen to a guy like me. I mean, look at you: You're beautiful. Now look at me. Women aren't exactly throwing themselves at me, okay?

Shit. I can't believe I just ... I'm sorry. I'll go. I'll leave you alone. I really didn't mean to offend you. I swear I didn't. *(Pause.)*

ISABEL. You think I'm beautiful?

JACK. Well. Yeah.

ISABEL. You know, Jack, I don't really see that many people.

JACK. It's kind of isolated out here.

ISABEL. No, I mean, I don't really go outside.

JACK. Why?

ISABEL. I don't know ... I mean, I never really liked going out in the first place. It's so hot. So lifeless. But lately, I can't even bring myself to leave the house. I get to the door and my legs just freeze.

So, you see, Jack, it isn't so strange. That I would ...

You're the best thing I've seen in a long, long time. *(Pause.)*

JACK. What's your name?

ISABEL. Isabel.

JACK. Isabel, can we start over?

ISABEL. I don't think so ...

JACK. Would you like to have dinner with me?

ISABEL. I just told you, I don't like going outside.

JACK. Who said anything about going outside? *(He gets a blanket off the couch and spreads it on the ground. He sets the box of pizza in the middle and opens it.)*

May I offer you a piece?

ISABEL. I would love one. *(She sits. He gives her a slice and then takes one himself. They each take a bite and chew quietly. She stops chewing.)*

JACK. What is it?

44

ISABEL. It just tastes so good.

Food tastes better when you eat it with someone, doesn't it?

JACK. It sure does.

Scene 19

The desert.

MAN. Are you cold?

Here. *(He takes off his jacket and gives it to her.)*

PANNY. I don't want it.

MAN. Please. Take it.

PANNY. Don't touch me.

MAN. Just thought you might be cold.

PANNY. Someone might have seen you. You could let me go, it's not too late.

MAN. You snuck out, didn't you?

PANNY. The guy I was meeting. He'll know.

MAN. Wasn't that him, leaving with your friend? Nice friend.

PANNY. Are you. Going to hurt me?

MAN. No.

PANNY. Please. Please don't do this.

MAN. Do what? I'm not doing anything. We're just talking.

PANNY. Are you the same guy who … took those other girls?

MAN. Maybe.

PANNY. You must be pretty smart, not to get caught.

MAN. I am smart.

PANNY. They were pretty, those girls.

MAN. Yes, they were.

PANNY. I don't understand. I'm not like that.

MAN. I'll tell you a secret. Just between us. You were an accident. I came tonight to see Nancy. I was finally going to introduce myself to her. But just my luck, she runs into that boy of yours. And before I know it, he's spirited her away in his car. You can imagine, it came as quite a shock. All that time and planning …

But then, luckily, there was you.

PANNY. But all the girls you take. They all look the same, right?

I'm not your type. If you let me go, I won't tell anyone, I swear. I wouldn't get you in trouble. I like you.

MAN. And I like you. But it's true, Panny, you're not my type.

PANNY. *(With relief.)* No, I'm not. *(He takes out a plastic bag and hands it to Panny.)*

What is this?

MAN. It's for you. Always be prepared. That's my motto, I say. *(Panny opens the bag and takes out a blonde wig.)*

I want you to put it on.

Panny?

Oh, now, Panny. Why're you crying?

You might as well just put it on. *(He leans in closer. He pats her arm as if to comfort her.)*

Because I seriously doubt anyone even knows you're gone.

Scene 20

Evvie's apartment.

EVVIE. I feel giddy.

LEFTY. Me too.

EVVIE. Are we really doing this?

LEFTY. Yes.

EVVIE. I'm not nervous.

LEFTY. No reason to be.

EVVIE. Come back quick. If you're gone for too long, I'll start to think you've changed your mind.

LEFTY. I'll just go get my things, tell Panny — you'll like her. I know you will.

EVVIE. Yes.

LEFTY. She'll get used to the idea, eventually she'll be okay with it.

EVVIE. She'll understand.

LEFTY. She'll like it here.

EVVIE. Welcome any time.

LEFTY. And eventually she'll *want* to live here.

EVVIE. And she'll — Why would she want to do that?

LEFTY. Because she ... because she will. Live here.

EVVIE. What?

LEFTY. Won't she?

EVVIE. Lefty. Lefty. She can't — I mean, I'd like you to be here. But I mean just you.

LEFTY. Oh.

EVVIE. I'm not ready to be a ... a ... mother figure again. I just got through with that. I just assumed ... I mean, Panny will stay with her mom, right?

LEFTY. No ... it's not that simple. Her mother isn't really able to take care of her.

EVVIE. Well, I'm not able to right now either. I mean, you that's different. But a kid ...

LEFTY. I can't leave Panny.

EVVIE. I wouldn't ask you to.

LEFTY. I want to be with you.

EVVIE. I want that too.

LEFTY. But I want a family.

EVVIE. What do you mean by "family"? You mean kids?

LEFTY. Yes.

EVVIE. You have a kid.

LEFTY. Yes, but ... not one of my own.

(Pause. For once, Evvie has no idea what to say.)

EVVIE. I ... I ...

LEFTY. Not now, it doesn't have to be now. Later, after we see how we are together.

EVVIE. But ... After Jess, I knew I didn't want any more ... That's what I meant about living for me now. Do you understand? *(Lefty nods. Long pause. They both look a little sad and perplexed.)*

So now what?

LEFTY. I don't know.

(Beat.)

EVVIE. Huh.

(Beat.)

LEFTY. Huh.

(Beat.)

EVVIE. Huh.

Scene 21

The living room. Isabel and Jack are sprawled on the floor.

JACK. I am so … totally … fired.

ISABEL. It's only been an hour.

JACK. I had two more deliveries to make.

ISABEL. You mean there's more pizzas in there? *(She opens the warmer and takes one out.)*

JACK. You're hungry again?

ISABEL. Aren't you? *(Jack starts getting dressed.)*
    Where are you going?

JACK. Where do you think? Work. Maybe I can talk them out of firing my sorry ass. What do you think — flat tire? Held up at knife point? Maybe I should give myself a cut.

ISABEL. When will I see you again?

JACK. … Soon.

ISABEL. You hesitated, why did you hesitate?

JACK. I didn't — look, don't worry. I'll come see you again.

ISABEL. Are you sure? *(He kisses her forehead.)*

JACK. Just chill.

ISABEL. I don't want you to disappear, I don't want it to be like this never —

JACK. Now where's my warmer?

ISABEL. How about tomorrow night?

JACK. Tomorrow's bad.

ISABEL. Then how about after that?

JACK. I don't know. I'll call you.

ISABEL. Do you have my number?

JACK. Sure, it's on the computer down at the parlor.

ISABEL. So you'll call me?

JACK. Absolutely.

ISABEL. I have a crazy idea: Maybe you could take me with you.

JACK. What?

ISABEL. I could be ready, I could try —

JACK. And where'm I supposed to take you? To my parents?

ISABEL. I just thought that maybe with your help I could —

48

JACK. We'll talk about this later, okay? I really gotta go.

Now about the money?

ISABEL. The what?

JACK. For the pizza. *(Isabel finds the twenty and gives it to him.)*

Thanks. Don't worry, Mirabelle. I'll be back. *(He leaves. She opens the door.)*

ISABEL. *(Calling.)* It's Isabel. Isabel! How are you going to call me if you don't have my name right? Jack. Jack! *(She watches him drive away. She slumps against the doorframe. The General appears. He squares the hat on his head. He picks up his suitcase. He throws his scarf around his neck. He salutes. He leaves.)*

Scene 22

The desert. Panny is wearing the blonde wig.

MAN. Fantastic sky. I love it out here. Away from all the street-lights you can see so many stars.

Tell me a little about yourself. Do you have a boyfriend?

PANNY. No.

MAN. Are you a good girl?

PANNY. Yes.

MAN. I think you're lying.

Have you ever been kissed?

PANNY. No.

(He kisses her.)

MAN. Did you like that?

I said, *Did you like that?*

PANNY. Yes.

MAN. Would you like another?

PANNY. Yes.

MAN. Yes what?

PANNY. Yes please. *(He leans in to kiss her. They freeze.)*

(To us:) And that's when I gouged out his eyes.

I planted my thumbs on his eyelids and I pushed, as hard as I could. Just like they taught us in self-defense. He screamed and I rolled away from him. I started running and I didn't stop. There was blood on my hands but I didn't stop. I ran straight for the first lights I saw. I ran and I ran until I got away. *(Hae-Yoon appears.)*

HAE-YOON. But, my little American friend, this is not the thing what happen.

PANNY. Yes, it is.

HAE-YOON. That is what the wish for what happen was, no? You wish you had gouge out evil pervert's eyes. You wish you had run away. Escape with no bad thing on you.

PANNY. I did.

HAE-YOON. You know in Korea how girl and guy meet? Guy in car will drive by a girl and say to her, "Ya! Ta!" Which mean, "Get in the car now!" And she will. But that is not dangerous because everyone do that. She get in, they talk, if they do not like each other, she get out and he go and find another girl. That how you maybe meet good person to marry. Because we are so ... pressed on. No, wait. *Re*pressed. That is what I mean.

But anyway, in Korea, you can do this because no psycho bad guy take you out to BFE and cut you up.

But in America, I could have told you, stupid nut, do not get in guy's car! Haven't you seen *Silence of the Lambs*? Don't you know Ted Bundy??? DON'T GET IN THE CAR. I am not even American and I know this. Sheeeesh. *(Rewind. The Man is about to kiss Panny. She puts her hands on the sides of his face. She puts her thumbs on his eyes and presses.)*

MAN. FUCK! *(He stands up and knocks her down.)*

HAE-YOON. *(Softly.)* No, my American friend, you just made him mad. *(She fades away. The Man holds his hands to his eyes. He takes his hands down. He stares at Panny as the lights on him fade.)*

MAN. Shit. That fucking hurt.

(The Man is gone.)

PANNY. *(To us:)* It's like I said. Things happen all the time, things you can't explain. Like Sheila Lopez ... like keg parties ... like Mr. Lindhart and.

Every once in awhile, something bad ... A guy takes a girl out there ...

There are still rumors swirling about what happened to me ... That I ... or that I ...

But none of those things are true. What is true, depends, like Sheila, her mom, and the light in the sky on which way you are facing.

The truth is, I didn't escape. He beat me senseless and when I came to, he was gone. He didn't kill me. I wasn't his type. I was too ugly, even for him.

He carved it into me. See? *(She raises her shirt. There is a scar. It spells out: "UGLY." She puts her shirt down.)*

That's how I know.

Scene 23

PANNY. Dear Elizabeth.

I am very sorry it's been so long since I last wrote. Things have been very busy. I'm okay now. Please understand that it's just been a little hectic.

By the way, I went ahead and had that surgery done on my eyes. *(As she talks, she puts gauze on her eyes and puts on a pair of dark sunglasses.)*

During the surgery, it was so strange. I had a dream while I was being operated on. I dreamed that there were these blue, round birds all over the house. They were sitting on the chairs, the tables, the lamps. But they couldn't fly very well; they were big, like balloons filled with water. And I dreamed that I went through the house with a long, steel needle, and I pierced these birds and the blood ran out of them.

I don't know what that means.

(Lights shift. The living room. Panny sits down.)

Lefty?

Isabel?

Can someone get me some water?

I need to take my pills. It's starting to hurt now. *(The doorbell rings.)*

Someone get the door? *(Lefty enters. He opens the door. Hugo stands there holding a bouquet of flowers.)*

HUGO. Is Panny here?

LEFTY. What's your name?

HUGO. It's Hugo.

LEFTY. *(To Panny.)* You know a Hugo? *(Panny nods. Lefty lets him in. Hugo slowly places the flowers in Panny's arms and she buries her face in them. Lefty leaves. Hugo stares at Panny.)*

PANNY. How'd you find me?

HUGO. Nancy.

PANNY. Does the whole school know?

HUGO. There are rumors. The news reports didn't use your name, but Nancy put two and two together.

PANNY. Oh.

HUGO. What happened to your eyes?

PANNY. Nothing. I just ... had some eye surgery and I had a bad reaction. I'm fine, but all swollen up. Practically swollen shut. But the doctor says the swelling will go down and then it'll be fine. That's all.

HUGO. Why did you need surgery? Did he hurt them?

PANNY. No. It was my choice. I wanted ... a change.

Do you hate me?

HUGO. No.

Do you hate me?

PANNY. No.

I'm glad you're here.

HUGO. I can't stay long.

PANNY. I know.

It wasn't a trick.

I meant all of it.

HUGO. I know.

Is there anything I can do for you before I go?

PANNY. Yeah. I. *(Pause.)* There's a glass of water over there. Do you see it? Could you get it for me? *(Hugo gets her the glass of water and hands it to her. She feels for his arm and touches it. She takes the water. She drinks. As she drinks he quietly leaves.)*

Thank you.

Hugo?

Hugo. *(All is still. Red tears start to stream down Panny's face from behind her glasses.)*

LEFTY. Panny? Are you okay?

Where'd your friend go? Panny?

PANNY. Don't look at me, Lefty. Just don't look.

Scene 24

Lights up on Lefty, Isabel and Panny. They are watching TV.

HAE-YOON. Dear Panny,

I like your last letter very much, but somehow, I don't know why, after I read it I feel a little sad. Like a heavy little thing in my chest. So I am sending you things for cheering you up.

First, this is a picture of my dog, Paachi. He is fat like this because my mother feed him too much. She say it is my father's fault for not walking him. But father say, Paachi is so fat, he is ashamed to be seen by neighbors with him. My brother is also fat. My father is ashamed to be seen with him too. Sometime, he goes pee right in the house (Paachi, not my brother) and then my father's face turns very red and he yell until he lose his voice.

Second, this is a tape of my favorite Korean pop songs. You will like first song, "I Will Love You Until You Are Dead and Then a Little More."

Third, I have good joke for you:

Why did the cow roll down the hill?

Because it had no leg!

(I think maybe this joke is funnier in Korean.)

So cheering up, my friend. Remember, you are in America! How can life be bad?

Your friend,

Elizabeth.

(The phone rings. They each look at it for a moment. No one picks it up. They watch TV.)

End of Play

PROPERTY LIST

Lefty's security guard uniform
Framed photo of Evvie's daughter
Water machine
Phone on Panny's bedstand
Pizza warmer
Gauze for eyes
Magazine (PANNY)
Items to be stored on drugstore shelf (NANCY)
Walkman (MAN)
Box (NANCY)
Blue airmail envelope (LEFTY, PANNY)
Birthday cake with icing and candle (LEFTY)
Sunmaid raisin box (LEFTY)
Sparkly earrings on plastic square (PANNY)
Yellow Pages phone book (PANNY and ISABEL)
Tray of food (PANNY)
Model of a battleground with miniature warriors (LEFTY)
Notepad (PANNY)
Book (EVVIE)
Return receipt (LEFTY, EVVIE)
Name badge (EVVIE)
Juice carton (HUGO)
Phone (HUGO)
Large textbook (HUGO)
White gloves (GENERAL MacARTHUR)
Miniature warrior (LEFTY)
Paperback book (ISABEL)
Fashion magazine (ISABEL)
Large empty water bottle (MAN)
Quarters (MAN)
Man's handkerchief (MAN, PANNY)
Woman's purse (ISABEL)
Twenty-dollar bill (LEFTY, ISABEL, JACK)
Tape player (ISABEL)
Bottle of wine, two glasses (ISABEL)
Name tag for Jack (ISABEL)
Blanket from couch (JACK)
2 pizzas (JACK, ISABEL)
Slices of pizza (ISABEL, JACK)

Man's jacket (MAN)
Blonde wig (MAN, PANNY)
Suitcase (GENERAL MacARTHUR)
General's hat and scarf (GENERAL MacARTHUR)
Sunglasses (GENERAL MacARTHUR)
Bouquet of flowers (HUGO)
Glass of water for Panny (HUGO)

SOUND EFFECTS

Opening strains to theme of a soap opera
Doorbell
Loud sound of water filling water bottle